Joseph Haydn

Symphony No. 94 in G major / G-Dur

Hob. I:94 Surprise / Mit dem Paukenschlag

Edited by / Herausgegeben von
Harry Newstone

Urtext

EULENBURG

EAS 141
ISBN 978-3-7957-6541-5
ISMN M-2002-2365-1

Urtext edition based on Eulenburg Study Score ETP 435

Ernst Eulenburg Ltd
48 Great Marlborough Street
London W1F 7BB

Contents / Inhalt

	Preface	V	
	Vorwort	IX	
I.	Adagio – Vivace assai	1	Track 1

II.	Andante	26	Track 2

III.	Menuetto / Trio. Allegro molto	38	Track 3

IV.	Finale. Allegro di molto	44	Track 4

The Art of Score-Reading	67	
Die Kunst des Partiturlesens	79	

Preface

Composed: 1791/92 in London
First performance: 1792, London
Original publisher: André, Offenbach, 1795; Artaria, Vienna, 1795
Instrumentation: 2 flutes, 2 oboes, 2 bassoons – 2 horns, 2 trumpets – timpani – strings
Duration: ca. 23 minutes

In the autumn of 1790 Prince Nikolaus Joseph Esterházy, Haydn's employer and patron, died and his son, Prince Paul Anton, succeeded him. Almost at once the great (but considerably expensive) musical establishment which had for nearly thirty years nurtured the composer, and is now chiefly remembered for the glory he brought to it, was dismantled. Although still nominally Capellmeister, with a yearly pension, Haydn was at last free to travel wherever he wished, something he had not been able to do before. He returned to Vienna relieved of the daily pressures of court duties, but his respite was not to last long. Johann Peter Salomon, the German-born violinist and London impresario, was visiting Cologne when he heard of the death of Prince Nikolaus and lost no time in getting to Vienna determined to procure Haydn for his forthcoming London season. It was not the first time he had invited Haydn to England; now the composer was free to accept, and he did. A contract was exchanged and the two left Vienna in the middle of December and arrived in Dover on New Year's Day 1791.

Haydn stayed in England for a year and a half and returned for a second visit of similar duration in 1794-5. The stimulus he received from the London musical scene, the reception he was accorded there and the high quality of the musicians placed at his disposal inspired him to some of his finest music. The twelve symphonies he wrote for Salomon (six for each visit) are the summation of his orchestral achievement and the ground upon which the music he composed after his return to Vienna – notably the last six masses, *The Creation* and *The Seasons* – was based.

The most popular of the London symphonies are among the most frequently played of Haydn's works, yet for very many years they were (and often still are) performed from texts that had, during the 19th century, become seriously corrupted from the originals. The first modern attempt to present a uniform set of scores based upon authentic sources came with Ernst Praetorius's edition for Eulenberg in the 1930s. For this he consulted the autograph scores of Nos. 98, 99, 101, 102, 103 and 104 but not those of Nos. 94, 95, 96 and 100 (No. 93 has disappeared and the whereabouts of No.97 was then unknown). One can only speculate on why Praetorius was not able to examine the autograph of No.94 which was in the then Preußischen Staatsbibliothek in Berlin, where he had seen those of Nos. 98, 99, 101, 102 and 104, or Nos. 95 and 96 which were in the British Museum along with No. 103 of which he had received a photocopy. Clearly, detailed knowledge of the whereabouts of Haydn autographs was still very sketchy in the 1930s and Praetorius probably had no way of knowing what we, with the benefit of a further 50 years of Haydn research, can take for granted. Thus Praetorius's edition, while the best available at the time and certainly an important step in the right direction was, not surprisingly, uneven.

The phase of Haydn research that was to result in no less than a renaissance was now well begun. In 1939 the distinguished Danish scholar Jens Peter Larsen published *Die Haydn-Überlieferung* and two years later a facsimile print of *Drei Haydn-Kataloge*, revealing for the first time the immensity of the subject. The post-war years saw the formation in London of the Haydn Orchestra and in Boston of the Haydn Society (both 1949). In 1954, the founder of the Haydn Society, H.C. Robbins Landon, in an article *The original versions of Haydn's first 'Salomon' symphonies*, drew our attention to the extent to which the standard performing editions of these works (mostly Breitkopf & Härtel and Peters) were in many cases 'flagrant falsifications of Haydn's own texts'. For a discussion on how these alterations came about the reader is referred to that article as well as to Landon's *The Symphonies of Joseph Haydn*, and his *Haydn – Chronicle and Works*, Vol. 3 *Haydn in England.*

Since the mid-1950s Henle Verlag, Munich, has issued a number of volumes of Haydn symphonies as part of a Complete Edition of his works for the Haydn Institute of Cologne. Universal Edition, Vienna, issued all the symphonies during the 1960s in an edition by H. C. Robbins Landon.

In 1959, the present writer, with material and advice from Professor Landon, revised and conducted all the London symphonies in a series of BBC broadcasts commemorating the 150th anniversary of the composer's death. The aim was to get as close as possible to Haydn's original intentions not only from the scholar's point of view but from the performer's too.

The texts were accordingly prepared from a number of manuscript sources of primary authenticity and one early printed edition of unusual interest and importance. These same sources, which are listed below with their credentials, have been re-examined for this new edition together with other more recent discoveries.

Symphony No. 94

This symphony received its first performance in the Hanover Square Rooms, London, on 23 March at the sixth of Salomon's 1792 series of concerts. Salomon led the orchestra and Haydn directed from the keyboard. It was an enormous success and soon became one of Haydn's most popular symphonies. It remains so today.

The work's additional title, 'Surprise', refers to the loud chord in the second movement, bar 16, a passage that had originally been written without this effect. The name was not the composer's; credit for its invention was later claimed by the London flautist Andrew Ashe who reported that 'my valued friend Haydn thank'd me for giving it such an appropriate Name'. The Symphony is universally known as the 'Surprise' or, in Germany, by the description 'Mit dem Paukenschlag' (with the kettledrum stroke).

Harry Newstone (adapted)

Vorwort

Komponiert: 1791/92 in London
Uraufführung: 23. März 1792 in London
Originalverlag: André, Offenbach, 1795; Artaria, Wien, 1795
Orchesterbesetzung: 2 Flöten, 2 Oboen, 2 Fagotte – 2 Hörner, 2 Trompeten – 2 Pauken – Streicher
Spieldauer: etwa 23 Minuten

Im Herbst 1790 starb Fürst Nikolaus Joseph Esterházy, Haydns Dienstherr und Gönner; Fürst Paul Anton, sein Sohn, folgte ihm nach. Fast unmittelbar hierauf wurde das bedeutende, allerdings ziemlich kostspielige Musikleben am Hofe eingestellt, das Haydn nahezu dreißig Jahre lang ernährt hatte und an das man sich heute hauptsächlich des Glanzes wegen erinnert, den es durch den Komponisten erhalten hatte. Obwohl er auch weiterhin den Kapellmeistertitel führen durfte und eine jährliche Pension erhielt, konnte Haydn im Gegensatz zu früher nun schließlich nach Belieben reisen. Er kehrte nach Wien zurück, entlastet vom täglichen Zwang des Dienstes am Hofe, jedoch sollte diese Ruhepause nicht von langer Dauer sein. Als der deutschstämmige Geiger und Londoner Impresario Johann Peter Salomon während eines Aufenthaltes in Köln vom Tod des Fürsten Nikolaus erfuhr, eilte er unverzüglich nach Wien, entschlossen, Haydn für die kommende Saison nach London zu verpflichten. Dies war nicht das erste Mal, dass er Haydn nach England eingeladen hatte; jetzt jedoch war der Komponist in der Lage zuzusagen, und er tat es auch. Ein Vertrag wurde ausgehandelt, und die beiden verließen Wien Mitte Dezember und erreichten Dover am Neujahrstag 1791.

Haydn blieb anderthalb Jahre lang in England und kehrte 1794/95 zu einem zweiten, etwa gleich langen Aufenthalt zurück. Die Anregungen, die er durch das Londoner Musikleben erhielt, die Aufnahme dort und die hohe Qualität der ihm zur Verfügung stehenden Musiker inspirierten ihn zu mehreren seiner bedeutendsten Werke. So bilden die zwölf Sinfonien für Salomon (sechs für jeden Aufenthalt) die Zusammenfassung seiner ganzen Kunst der Orchesterkomposition und die Grundlage für die Werke, die er nach seiner Rückkehr nach Wien schrieb – vor allem die sechs letzten Messen sowie die *Schöpfung* und die *Jahreszeiten*.

Die bekanntesten der Londoner Sinfonien gehören zu den meistgespielten Werken Haydns, jedoch wurden sie viele Jahre lang (vielfach noch bis in die heutige Zeit) aus Notenmaterial aufgeführt, das im 19. Jahrhundert gegenüber dem Originaltext erheblich verfälscht worden war. Den ersten neueren Versuch, aufgrund der authentischen Quellen einen einheitlichen Satz Partituren herauszubringen, stellt die Ausgabe von Ernst Praetorius im Rahmen der

Edition Eulenburg in den 1930er Jahren dar. Er zog die Partitur-Autographe von Nr. 98, 99, 101, 102, 103 und 104 heran. Nicht aber diejenigen von Nr. 94, 95, 96 und 100 (das Autograph von Nr. 93 ist verschollen, und das von Nr. 97 war damals nicht nachweisbar). Man kann nur Vermutungen darüber anstellen, warum Praetorius nicht in der Lage war, das Autograph von Nr. 94 zu untersuchen, das in der damaligen Preußischen Staatsbibliothek in Berlin lag, wo er auch die Autographe von Nr. 98, 99, 101, 102 und 104 eingesehen hatte; Nr. 95 und 96 waren ihm im British Museum London zugänglich, zusammen mit dem Autograph von Nr. 103, das ihm als Fotokopie vorlag. Auf jeden Fall war die Kenntnis der Aufbewahrungsorte von Haydn-Autographen in den 1930er Jahren noch sehr lückenhaft, und Praetorius konnte damals wohl kaum wissen, was wir heute, nach weiteren 50 Jahren Haydn-Forschung, als erwiesen betrachten können. So war es nicht verwunderlich, dass die Ausgaben von Praetorius in sich uneinheitlich waren, auch wenn sie zu ihrer Zeit die besten verfügbaren waren und sicherlich einen Schritt in die richtige Richtung unternahmen.

Damit hatte eine Zeit intensiver Haydn-Forschung begonnen, die eine regelrechte Renaissance auslöste. 1939 veröffentlichte der bedeutende dänische Musikwissenschaftler Jens Peter Larsen sein Buch *Die Haydn-Überlieferung* und zwei Jahre später als Faksimile *Drei Haydn-Kataloge*; damit wies er erstmals auf die nahezu unüberschaubaren Dimensionen dieses Forschungsbereichs hin. In den Nachkriegsjahren folgten die Gründung des Haydn-Orchesters London und in Bosten die der Haydn-Gesellschaft (beide 1949), 1954 machte H.C. Robbins Landon, Begründer der Haydn-Gesellschaft, in einem Aufsatz *The original versions of Haydn's first 'Salomon' symphonies* auf das Ausmaß aufmerksam, in dem das verfügbare Aufführungsmaterial dieser Werke (hauptsächlich von Breitkopf & Härtel und Peters) in vielen Fällen durch „offenkundige Verfälschung von Haydns eigenem Notentext" entstellt war. Bezüglich einer eingehenden Darstellung, wie es zu diesen Abweichungen kam, sei hier auf den Aufsatz sowie auf Landons Arbeiten *The Symphonies of Joseph Haydn* und *Haydn – Chronicle and Works* (Bd. 3 *Haydn in England*) hingewiesen.

Seit Mitte der 1950er Jahre hat der Henle-Verlag München im Rahmen einer Gesamtausgabe der Werke Haydns durch das Institut Köln mehrere Bände mit Sinfonien veröffentlicht. Bei der Universal Edition Wien erschienen alle Sinfonien in den 1960er Jahren in einer Ausgabe von H.C. Robbins Landon.

1959 revidierte der Herausgeber der hier vorliegenden Ausgabe anlässlich einer Sendereihe der BBC zum 150. Todestage des Komponisten, in der er selbst alle Londoner Sinfonien Haydns dirigierte, die Partituren, wofür ihm Robbins Landon eigenes Material und seinen Rat zur Verfügung stellte. Das Ziel war, Haydns eigenen Intentionen nicht nur vom wissenschaftlichen Standpunkt aus, sondern auch aus der Sicht des ausübenden Musikers, so nahe wie möglich zu kommen.

Der Notentext wurde aufgrund einer Anzahl handschriftlicher Primärquellen und einer besonders interessanten und wichtigen Druckausgabe erarbeitet. Diese unten verzeichneten und beschriebenen Quellen wurden für die Neuausgabe unter Berücksichtigung anderer neuerer Forschungsergebnisse nochmals untersucht.

Sinfonie Nr. 94

Diese Sinfonie wurde zum ersten Mal in den Hanover Square Rooms, London, am 23. März im Rahmen des sechsten Konzerts der 1792 von Salomon gegebenen Konzertreihe unter der Leitung von Haydn als Cembalist und mit Salomon als Konzertmeister aufgeführt. Sie hatte außerordentlichen Erfolg und wurde bald zu einer der bis heute beliebtesten Sinfonien Haydns.

Die englische Bezeichnung „Surprise" bezieht sich auf den *fortissimo*-Akkord im II. Satz, Takt 16, eine Passage, die ursprünglich ohne diesen Effekt geschrieben war. Der Name stammt nicht vom Komponisten; ihn gefunden zu haben wurde später vom Londoner Flötisten Andrew Ashe beansprucht, der berichtete, dass „mein geschätzter Freund Haydn mir dafür dankte, dass ich ihr [der Sinfonie] einen angemessenen Namen gab." Bis heute ist die Sinfonie allgemein als „Surprise" oder auf Deutsch als „Sinfonie mit dem Paukenschlag" bekannt.

Harry Newstone (neu bearbeitet)

Symphony No. 94
'Surprise' / Mit dem Paukenschlag

Joseph Haydn
(1732–1809)
Hob. I:94

I. Adagio

6
Fl.
Ob.
Fg.
Solo
Cor. (G)
Tr. (C)
Timp.
Vl.
Vla.
Vc.
Cb
12
[a2]
cresc.
EAS 141

Vivace assai
18
[a2]
Fl.
Ob.
Fg
Tutti
Cor. (G)
Tr (C)
Timp
Vl.
Vla.
Vc
Cb.
22
Fl
Ob
Fg.
Cor. (G)
Tr. (C)
Timp.
Vl
Vla.
Vc.
Cb.

26
Fl.
Ob.
Fg.
Cor. (G)
Tr. (C)
Timp.
Vl.
Vla.
Vc.
Cb.
30
Fl.
Ob.
Fg.
Cor. (G)
Tr. (C)
Timp.
Vl.
fz
Vla.
fz
Vc.
Cb.
[fz]

34
Fl.
Ob.
Fg.
[Solo]
Cor. (G)
Tr. (C)
Timp.
Vl.
pizz.
Vla.
Vc.
Cb.
39
1. Solo
[a2]
arco
[fz]
[p]

45
Fl.
Ob.
Fg
Cor. (G)
Tr. (C)
Timp.
Vl
Vla.
Vc.
Cb.
fz
50
Fl.
Ob.
Fg.
Cor. (G)
Tr. (C)
Timp.
Vl.
Vla
Vc.
Cb.
fz

54
Fl.
Ob.
1. Solo
p
Fg.
Cor (G)
Tr. (C)
Timp.
Vl
p
p
Vla.
Vc.
Cb
59
Fl
f
Ob.
f
fz
fz
Fg.
f
fz
fz
Cor. (G)
f
Tr (C)
f
Timp
f
Vl.
f
f
fz
fz
f
fz
fz
Vla.
f
fz
fz
Vc.
Cb
f
fz
fz

63
Fl.
Ob.
Fg.
Cor. (G)
Tr. (C)
Timp.
Vl.
Vla.
Vc.
Cb.
69
Solo
[p]
fz
p

73
Fl.
Ob.
Fg.
Cor. (G)
Tr. (C)
Timp.
Vl.
Vla.
Vc.
Cb.
[a2]
f
77
Vc.
Cb.
[muta G in A]
p
dolce
tr

84
Fl.
Ob
Fg.
Cor. (G)
Tr. (C)
Timp.
Vl.
Vla
Vc.
Cb
Solo
1.
Solo
pizz.
90
Fl
Ob.
Fg
Cor. (G)
Tr. (C)
Timp.
Vl.
Vla.
Vc
Cb
[p]

96
Fl.
Ob.
Fg.
Cor (G)
Tı. (C)
Timp.
Vl.
Vla.
Vc
Cb.
[a2]
[a2]
arco
101
Fl
Ob.
a2
Fg.
Cor. (G)
Tı. (C)
Timp
Vl.
Vla.
Vc.
Cb

108
[a2]
Fl.
1. Solo
a2
Ob
[p] dolce
[a2]
Fg.
Cor. (G)
Tr. (C)
[f]
Timp
Vl.
Vla.
Vc.
Cb.
113
Fl.
Ob.
Solo
Fg.
Vl.
Vla
Vc.
Cb.

119
Fl.
Ob.
Fg.
Cor. (G)
Tr. (C)
Timp.
Vl.
Vla.
Vc.
Cb.
125
a2
[a2]

131
Fl
Ob
Fg.
Cor. (G)
Tr. (C)
Timp
Vl.
Vla.
Vc
Cb
137
[a2]
[muta A in G]

142
Fl.
Ob.
Fg.
Vl
Vla.
Vc.
Cb
fz
146
[fz]
Cor. (G)
f

152
Fl.
Ob.
Fg.
Cor. (G)
Vl.
Vla.
Vc.
Cb.
Solo
1.
158
[a2]
Fl.
Ob
Fg.
Cor. (G)
Tr. (C)
Timp
Vl
Vla.
Vc
Cb.

162
Fl.
Ob.
Fg.
Cor (G)
Tr. (C)
Timp
Vl.
Vla.
Vc.
Cb
166
Fl.
Ob.
Fg.
Cor (G)
Tr (C)
Timp
Vl.
fz
Vla.
fz
Vc.
Cb.
[fz]

170
Fl
Ob.
Fg.
Cor. (G)
Tr. (C)
Timp
Vl.
Vla
Vc.
Cb.
174
Fl
ff
Ob
a2
ff
Fg.
ff
Cor. (G)
ff
Tr. (C)
Timp.
Vl.
Vla.
Vc.
Cb.

178
Fl
Ob.
Fg.
Cor (G)
Tr. (C)
Timp.
Vl.
Vla.
Vc.
Cb.
184
Fl.
Ob.
Fg.
Vl.
Vla.
Vc.
Cb.

189
Fl.
Ob.
[a2]
Fg.
Cor. (G)
Tr (C)
Timp.
Vl.
Vla.
Vc
Cb
193
Fl.
Ob
Fg
Cor (G)
Tr (C)
Timp
Vl.
Vla
Vc
Cb.

198
Fl.
Ob.
Fg.
Cor. (G)
Timp.
Vl.
Vla.
Vc
Cb.
Solo
204
Fl.
Ob
Fg.
Cor (G)
Timp
Vl
Vla.
Vc.
Cb.

210
[a2]
Fl.
Ob.
Fg.
Cor. (G)
Tr (C)
Timp.
Vl.
Vla.
Vc.
Cb.
216
Solo
1.
Solo
[fz]

223
Fl.
[fz]
Ob.
1.
Fg
Vl
p
Vla
Vc.
Cb.
229
Fl
Ob.
Fg
Vl
[dolce]
tr
Vla
Vc
Cb

235
Fl.
1. Solo
Ob.
[p] dolce
Fg.
p
Cor. (G)
pp
Vl.
Vla.
pizz.
Vc.
Cb
241
Solo
Fl.
[p]
fz fz fz fz fz
Ob
[p]
fz fz fz fz fz
Fg.
Vl.
p
p
Vla.
p
Vc.
Cb.

247
Fl
Ob
Fg.
Cor. (G)
Tr. (C)
Timp.
Vl.
Vla
Vc.
Cb.
[a2]
a2
arco
252
Fl.
Ob.
Fg.
Cor. (G)
Tr. (C)
Timp.
Vl.
Vla.
Vc.
Cb.

II. Andante

Flauto 1 2
Oboe 1 2
Fagotto 1 2
Corno (C) 1 2
Tromba (C) 1 2
(Clarino)
Timpani (C G)
Violino I
Violino II
Viola
Violoncello
e Contrabbasso
semplice
ten.
p
pp
pizz.
8
Vl.
Vla.
Vc
Cb

16
[a2]
Fl
Ob.
[a2]
Fg.
Cor. (C)
Tr (C)
Timp
Vl.
Vla
Vc
Cb.
ff
arco
p
ten.
23
Solo
1.
Fl.
Ob.
Cor (C)
Vl
Vla
Vc.
Cb
p

29
Fl.
Ob.
Fg.
Cor (C)
Tr (C)
Timp.
Vl.
Vla.
Vc.
Cb
1.
ten.
[a2]
f
p
fz
36
Solo
[fz]
41

47
Fl.
Ob.
Fg.
Vl.
Vla
Vc
Cb.
[a2]
ten.
a2
[Solo]
55
[a2]
59
Vla.
Vc.
Cb

63
Fl
Ob
Fg
Tr (C)
Timp
f
f
Vl
Vla
Vc
Cb
66
Fl.
Ob
Fg.
Tr (C)
Timp
Vl
Vla
Vc
Cb

69
Fl.
Ob.
Fg
Ti (C)
Timp
Vl.
Vla.
Vc.
Cb
p
75
Fl
Ob
Solo
[p]
ten.
ten.
Fg
[Solo]
p
Vl.
p
Vla.
p
Vc
Cb.
p

80
Solo
Fl.
Ob.
Fg.
Vl.
Vla.
Vc.
Cb.
ten.
[p]
pp
86
fz
92

98
1.
Fl.
Ob
Cor. (C)
p
Vl.
Vla.
Vc
Cb
104
[a2]
f
Fg.
Tr (C)
ff
Timp.
ten.
6
Vla
Vc.
Cb.

109
Fl
Ob
Fg.
Cor. (C)
Tr. (C)
Timp
Vl
6
6
Vla
Vc.
Cb
113
3
3
3
3
Fl
Ob
[Solo]
Fg.
p
Cor. (C)
Tr. (C)
Timp
pianissimo e dolce
Vl
p
p
Vla.
p
Vc
Cb
p

118
[1.]
ten.
Fg.
Vl
Vla.
Vc.
Cb
124
[1.]
Fg
Vl
Vla
Vc.
Cb.
130
Fl
Ob.
[1.]
[a2]
Fg
Cor. (C)
Timp.
Vl.
Vla.
Vc.
Cb.
f

135
Fl
Ob.
Fg
Cor. (C)
Tr. (C)
Timp
Vl.
Vla.
Vc.
Cb
ten
ten.
139
Fl.
Ob
Fg.
Cor. (C)
Tr. (C)
Timp
Vl.
Vla.
Vc
Cb.
p

144
Solo
Fl.
[Solo]
Ob.
ten.
p
Solo
Fg.
pp
Cor. (C)
Timp
Vl.
[pp]
Vla.
Vc
Cb
150
1.
Timp.
Vla
Vc.
Cb.

III. Menuetto

Allegro molto

16
Fl
Ob
Fg
Cor. (G)
Tr (C)
Timp.
Vl.
Vla
Vc.
Cb
22
Fl
Ob.
Fg
Cor (G)
Tr (C)
Timp
Vl
p
p
f
Vla
Vc.
Cb

28
Fl.
Ob.
Fg.
Cor (G)
Tr (C)
Timp.
Vl.
Vla.
Vc.
Cb.
35
Solo
[Solo]
[a2]
Tutti

42
Fl.
Ob.
Fg.
Cor. (G)
Tr. (C)
Timp.
Vl.
Vla.
Vc
Cb.
Soli
p
50
Solo
p dolce
[a2]
Timp
[dolce]
fz
Vc.
Cb

57
[a2]
Fl.
Ob
Fg.
Cor (G)
Tr (C)
Timp.
Vl.
Vla
Vc
Cb
Trio
Solo
63
Fg.
[p] dolce
Vl.
p [dolce]
Vla.
Vc
Cb

71
Vl.
[sim]
Vla.
Vc.
Cb.
77
Fg.
1
p
fz
[p]
Vl.
fz
p
Vla.
Vc.
Cb.
83
1.
Fg
Vl.
Vla.
Vc
Cb.
Menuetto da capo

IV. Finale

Allegro di molto

14
Fl.
Vl.
Vla.
Vc.
Cb.
20
Vl.
Vla.
Vc.
Cb.
25
Vl.
Vla
Vc.
Cb.

30
Fl.
Fg
Vl
Vla
Vc
Cb
Solo
p [dolce]
Solo
[p] dolce
[dolce]
37
Fl
Ob.
Fg
Cor (G)
Tr (C)
Timp
Vl
Vla
Vc
Cb
1
[a2]
1.
[a2]
f
[fz]
fz
[fz]

43
Fl.
Ob
Fg.
Cor. (G)
Tr. (C)
Timp.
Vl
Vla.
Vc.
Cb.
48
Fl.
Ob.
Fg.
Cor. (G)
Tr. (C)
Timp.
Vl.
Vla.
Vc.
Cb.

53
Fl.
Ob.
Fg.
Cor. (G)
Tr. (C)
Timp.
Vl.
Vla.
Vc.
Cb.
58
Fl.
Ob.
Fg.
Cor. (G)
Tr (C)
Timp.
Vl.
Vla.
Vc.
Cb.

63
Fl.
Ob.
Fg.
Cor. (G)
Tr. (C)
Timp.
Vl
Vla.
Vc
Cb
68
Fl.
Ob.
Fg.
Cor. (G)
Tr. (C)
Timp.
Vl
Vla
Vc.
Cb.

73
Fl.
Ob
Fg
Cor. (G)
Vl
Vla.
Vc.
Cb.
[Solo]
p
pp
p
p
pizz.
p
80
Solo
Fl.
Ob.
1.
Fg.
Vl.
Vla.
Vc.
Cb.
p
p
arco
p

87
[a2]
Fl.
Ob.
[a2]
Fg.
Cor. (G)
Tr (C)
Timp.
Vl
Vla
arco
Vc
Cb
92
Fl.
Ob
Fg.
Cor. (G)
Tr. (C)
Timp
Vl
Vla.
Vc.
Cb

97
Fl.
Ob.
Fg.
Solo
[p]
Cor (G)
Tr. (C)
Timp.
Vl
Vla.
Vc.
Cb.
p
105
1.
Tutti
f

112
Fl.
Ob.
Fg.
Cor. (G)
Tr. (C)
Timp.
Vl.
f
Vla
Vc
Cb.
117
Fl.
Ob.
Fg.
Cor. (G)
Tr. (C)
Timp.
Vl.
fz
Vla
fz
Vc.
Cb.
f
fz

122
Fl
Ob
Fg.
Cor (G)
Tr. (C)
Timp.
Vl
fz
Vla.
fz
Vc
Cb.
fz
127
Fl.
Ob
Fg.
Vl.
Vla.
Vc
Cb

132
Fl.
Ob.
Fg.
Cor (G)
Vl
Vla.
Vc.
Cb.
137
Fl.
Ob.
Fg
Cor. (G)
Vl.
p
p
Vla.
p
Vc.
Cb.
p

143
Solo
Fl.
[p] dolce
Fg
Vl.
pp
[p] [dolce]
p
Vla.
Vc.
Cb.
150
1.
Tutti
Ob.
Cor. (G)
Tr. (C)
Timp.
f
fz

157
Fl.
Ob
Fg.
ff
Vl.
fz
Vla.
Vc.
Cb.
163
Cor. (G)
Tr. (C)
Timp.

168
Fl
Ob
Fg.
Cor. (G)
Tr. (C)
Timp
Vl
Vla.
Vc.
Cb
a2
fz
173
Fl
Ob
Fg
Cor. (G)
Tr. (C)
Timp.
Vl
Vla
Vc.
Cb.
fz

178
Fl.
Ob.
Fg.
Vl.
Vla.
Vc.
Cb.
Solo
[p] dolce
Solo
[p] dolce
p
p
p
p
[dolce]
184
1.
1.
[Soli]
p
Fl.
Ob.
Fg.
Vl.
Vla.
Vc.
Cb.

191
Fl.
Ob.
Vl.
Vla.
Vc
Cb
197
[a2]
Fl
Ob.
Fg
[a2]
Cor. (G)
Tr. (C)
Timp
Vl.
Vla.
Vc.
Cb.

203
Fl.
Ob.
Fg.
[a2]
Cor. (G)
Tr. (C)
Timp.
Vl.
Vla.
Vc
Cb.
208
Fl.
Solo
p
Ob.
Fg.
Solo
p
Cor. (G)
p
Timp.
Vl.
p
p
Vla.
p
Vc.
Cb.
pizz.
p

215
1.
Fl.
[Solo]
Ob.
1.
Fg.
Cor. (G)
Vl.
Vla.
Vc.
Cb.
222
[a2]
Fl.
[dolce]
[dolce]
Ob.
[a2]
Fg.
dolce
Cor. (G)
Tr. (C)
Timp.
pizz.
Vl.
pizz.
Vla.
arco
Vc
Cb

228
Fl.
Ob.
Fg
Cor (G)
Tr. (C)
Timp
Vl.
Vla.
Vc
Cb
a2
[a2]
arco
arco
235
Fl.
Ob
Fg
Timp
Vl.
Vla.
Vc
Cb.

241
Fl.
Ob.
Fg.
Cor. (G)
Tr. (C)
Timp.
Vl.
Vla.
Vc.
Cb
247
Fl.
Ob.
Fg.
Cor. (G)
Tr. (C)
Timp.
Vl.
Vla.
Vc
Cb.

253
Fl
Ob.
Fg
Cor. (G)
Tr (C)
Timp
Vl.
Vla
Vc
Cb.
259
Fl
Ob
Fg
Cor (G)
Tr. (C)
Timp.
Vl.
Vla.
Vc.
Cb.

THE ART OF SCORE-READING

The first steps

A score contains the entire musical text of a musical work in order that the conductor and everyone who wants to study the piece more thoroughly can see exactly which passages are being played by the orchestra or ensemble. The parts of the individual instruments are arranged in such a way that all notes played at the same time are written one below the other.
Scores help to listen to, understand and interpret musical works. Those who only listen to music are unaware of many important details which, after some practice, become apparent when reading the score while listening to the music. The clear structure of the score helps to easily understand the compositional style and the characteristic features of a piece – this is a prerequisite not only for any analysis but also for the musician's own performance and interpretation.

The simplest method of score-reading is to read an individual part by concentrating on an individual part that can be heard particularly well. The most suitable pieces to begin with are concertos with solo instruments such as Beethoven's Romance in F major for violin and orchestra (example 1) or orchestral songs (with them, one may easily follow the text). Furthermore, in many classical orchestral works, it is quite easy to follow the lead part of the principal violin, or the bass part in baroque compositions for orchestra.

The next step is to try to change from one part to another and vice versa and follow the part that is leading. Little by little, you learn to find distinctive parts you hear in the score as well and follow them in the corresponding staff. This can be very easily tried out with Beethoven's Symphony No. 5 (example 2). To read the score, it is also helpful to count the bars. This technique is rather useful in the case of confusing or complex scores, such as those of contemporary music, and is particularly suitable when you do not want to lag behind in any case. It should be your aim, however, to eventually give up counting the bars and to read the score by first following individual parts and then going over to section-by-section or selective reading (see next page).

Example 1 · from: Romance for violin and orchestra in F major by Beethoven

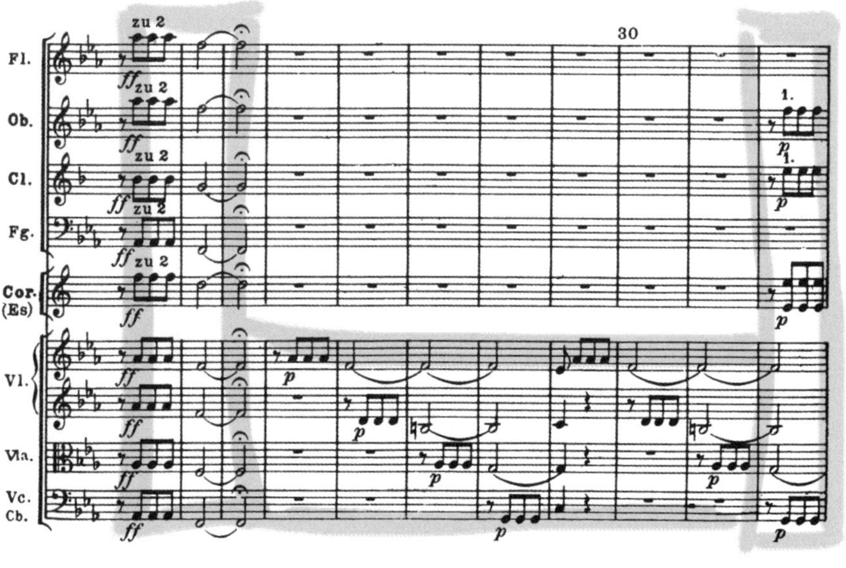

Example 2 · from: Symphony No. 5 C-minor by Beethoven

Further score-reading techniques

Example 3 · from: Symphony No. 100 G major 'Military' by Haydn

Example 4 · from: Symphony No. 41 C major 'Jupiter' by W. A. Mozart

Section-by-section reading

This technique is suitable for application in the 'Military' Symphony by Haydn (example 3). In bb. 260-264, the parts are mostly in parallel motion so that it is quite easy to take in the section as a whole. In the strings, the texture is homophonic (i.e. all instruments play the same rhythm), consisting of tone repetitions in the lower parts while there is a little more movement in the part of the first violin. At the same time, the tones of the winds are stationary (i.e. long sustained notes), serving as harmonic filling-in. If need be, they can also be read en bloc.

Such block-like structures often consist of unison figures (= all instruments play the same), such as at the beginning of Mozart's Jupiter Symphony (example 4). Here, the score-reading can first be limited to the strings section which carries the melody alone in bb. 3-4 and contains all important information.

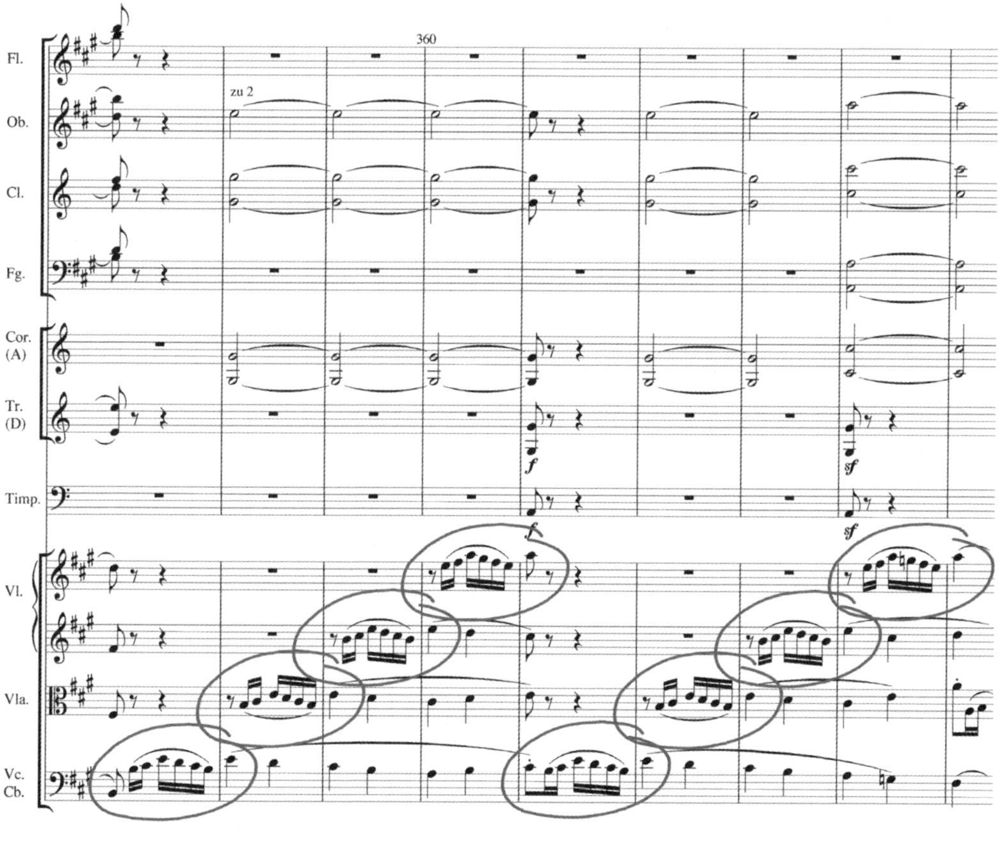

Example 5 · from: Symphony No. 7 A major by Beethoven

Selektive reading

Using this technique, you concentrate on selected parts (lead parts, conspicuous passages) in the score. In the excerpt from Beethoven's Symphony No. 7 (example 5), it is the semiquaver motif that, originating with the violoncellos and basses and pervading the string parts twice, is particularly well suited. The stationary tones of the winds, consisting only of the note E in various octave positions in bb. 358-363, form the harmonic foundation and play a subordinate role in score-reading. Though they are briefly noticed, it is the strings and especially the conspicuous semiquaver motif pervading the individual parts that are to be followed.

With both score-reading techniques which should be chosen according to the nature of the passage in question, it is not important in the beginning to be able to follow at once all tones and harmonies. What matters more is to recognize and comprehend sequences of movement. Everything else comes with experience.

Following contrapuntal parts

The present excerpt from Brahms's Requiem (example 6) is polyphonic, i.e. one has to be able to follow several equal parts either alternately (without lagging behind) or simultaneously. But by looking for parallel parts in the score, the notation which, at first glance, seems to be overcrowded soon becomes clearer. For example, Brahms allocates orchestral parts to each choral part. As a consequence, there are many parts written in the score but considerably fewer independent parts actually played. Hence, the large amount of written music can be reduced to a manageable quantity.

The flute, clarinet, first violins and soprano are in parallel motion. Furthermore, the tenor of oboe and viola is supported by a much-expanded, yet parallel part.
The violoncellos and bassoons too are in almost parallel motion.

The low winds and strings as well as the timpani played simultaneously with the polyphonic parts are fill-in parts which consist only of stationary tones (sustained notes). They do not need to be followed upon first reading of the score.

Seen as a whole, this excerpt is most suitable for focussing on the soprano voice as it is coupled with two instruments and, being the highest voice, can be heard very well. In addition, the text is an aid to orientation, making it easier to return from brief trips to other parts.

In fugal sections, score-reading will be easier if the entries of the theme in the score are first looked for and then marked.

Example 6 · from: A German Requiem by Brahms

The score at a glance

A **Bar lines** are solid vertical lines within the instrument sections.

B The **bar numbers** are an aid to orientation in the score. Sometimes capital letters, so-called rehearsal letters, are used instead of numbers.

C The system of parallel lines on and between which the notes are written is called **staff** (or stave). The instrument abbreviation in front of each line (here, Fl. is for 'flute') indicates to which instrument(s) the line(s) refer(s).

D The **barline at the left-hand end** of the staves connects all staves to form the **system**.

E In addition to the barline at the left-hand end of the staves, **angular brackets** connect the individual groups of instruments in a score (wind, brass and string instruments). Within these groups, the instruments are arranged according to their pitch, with the highest-pitched instrument mentioned first.
Today, the common order of instrumental parts in the score is as follows, from top to bottom:
· wind instruments
· brass instruments
· percussion instruments
· harp, piano, celesta
· solo instrument(s)
· solo voices
· choir
· string instruments

F When there are two systems on a page, they are separated from each other by two parallel **diagonal strokes**.

G Instruments the names of which are followed by 'in Bb' or (Bb) are **transposing instruments**. In this case, (Bb) indicates that the notated C is played as Bb, i.e. all tones are played a tone lower than notated. Most of the transposing instruments are easily recognizable in the score thanks to these additions. However, there are also transposing instruments without such indications in the score, such as:
· piccolo flute (in C / an octave higher)
· cor anglais (in F / a fifth lower)
· contrabassoon (in C / an octave lower)
· double bass (in C / an octave lower)

H The transposing brass instruments have no general signature but, if need be, accidentals preceding the respective tone.

I The viola part is notated in the **alto clef**, the parts of violoncello and bassoon sometimes in the **tenor clef**. Both clefs are easy to read when the player realizes that the clef frames the note C1:
alto clef tenor clef treble clef

J Any change of key or time is marked by a **double bar**. The alla-breve sign following in this example (¢), like the sign for four-four time (c), is a relic from an old notational practice and stands for two-two time.

B
A
C
4
29
Fl.
sfp
dim.
pp
D
Ob.
Cl. (B♭)
1.
E
Fag.
Cor. (B♭)
Vl.
I
II
arco
Vla.
Vc.
Cb.
F
34
G
H
Tr. (B♭)
Timp.
tr
ff
cresc.
I
J

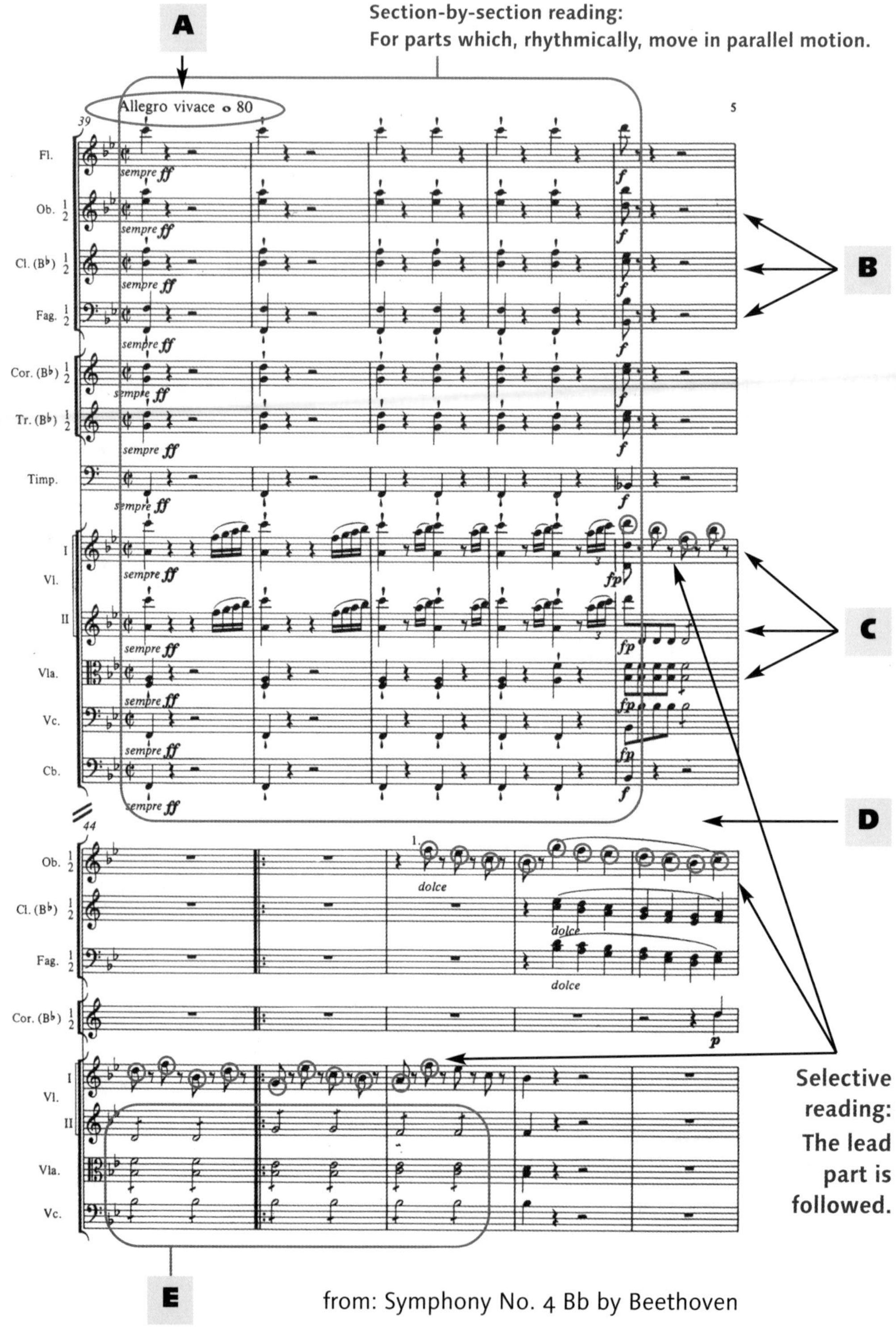

from: Symphony No. 4 Bb by Beethoven

A **Tempo indications** (sometimes in connection with metronome markings) are used by the composer to indicate how fast a piece shall be played.

B In the winds, two parts are usually brought together in one line. If they play the same note, the note head either has two stems or 'a2' written above it.

C Two-part chords in the staves of the strings are played by one player. If the parts shall be divided, **divisi** (divided) is written in the score. Then, at each desk, one player plays the upper notes and another player the lower notes.

D When an instrumental part contains a long rest, as in this flute part for example, its staff is often omitted until the next entry of the instrument, thus saving space. In addition, there are less page-turns, and the playing parts are arranged much clearer.

E In order to save space and arrange phrases or groups of notes more clearly, so-called abbreviations are used occasionally. The sign 𝅗𝅥 stands for ♩♩♩♩, with the minim indicating the duration of the repetitions and the stroke crossing the stem indicating the value of the notes to be repeated (1 stroke = quaver, 2 strokes = semiquaver, etc.). Cf. also the viola in b. 43 in which the repeated notes are first written out and then abbreviated.

DIE KUNST
DES PARTITURLESENS

Der erste Einstieg

Eine Partitur enthält den gesamten Notentext eines Musikwerkes, damit der Dirigent und jeder, der sich näher mit dem Stück beschäftigen will, genau nachvollziehen kann, was das Orchester oder das Ensemble spielt. Dabei sind die Instrumente so angeordnet, dass alle Noten, die zur gleichen Zeit erklingen, genau untereinander stehen.
Partituren helfen beim Hören, Begreifen und Interpretieren von Musikliteratur. Wer nur zuhört, erkennt viele kostbare Kleinigkeiten nicht, die beim Mitlesen nach ein wenig Übung regelrecht sichtbar werden. Der Kompositionsstil und die Charakteristik eines Werkes lassen sich mit der übersichtlichen Partitur schnell begreifen – das ist nicht nur Grundvoraussetzung für jede Analyse, sondern auch für das eigene Spiel.

Die einfachste Methode beim Partiturlesen ist das Verfolgen einer Einzelstimme. Bei diesem Verfahren konzentriert man sich auf eine einzelne Stimme, die besonders gut zu hören ist. Zum Einstieg eignen sich dabei besonders gut Konzerte mit Soloinstrumenten wie die Romanze in F-Dur für Violine und Orchester von Beethoven (Beispiel 1) oder Orchesterlieder (bei letzteren kann man sich leicht am Text orientieren). Weiterhin kann man bei vielen klassischen Orchesterwerken die führende Stimme der ersten Violine gut verfolgen, sowie bei barocken Kompositionen für Orchester die Bass-Stimme.

In einem nächsten Schritt kann man versuchen, zwischen den Stimmen zu wechseln und jeweils die Stimme zu verfolgen, die gerade führend ist. Nach und nach lernt man dabei markante Stimmen, die man hört, auch in der Partitur zu finden und im entsprechenden Notensystem zu verfolgen. Besonders anschaulich kann man das mittels Beethovens 5. Symphonie erproben (Beispiel 2).
Eine weitere Hilfe beim Lesen der Partitur kann auch das Mitzählen der Takte sein. Dieses Verfahren hilft bei unübersichtlichen oder komplexen Partituren wie etwa zeitgenössischer Musik und eignet sich besonders, wenn man den Anschluss auf keinen Fall verlieren möchte. Ziel sollte es jedoch sein, das Mitzählen der Takte gänzlich zu verlassen und die Partitur zunächst anhand einzelner Stimmen und dann im Wechsel von blockweisem bzw. selektivem Lesen zu verfolgen (siehe nächste Seite).

Beispiel 1 · aus: Romanze für Violine und Orchester F-Dur von Beethoven

Beispiel 2 · aus: Symphonie Nr. 5 c-moll von Beethoven

Weitere Methoden des Partiturlesens

Beispiel 3 · aus: Symphonie Nr. 100 G-Dur „Militär" von Haydn

Beispiel 4 · aus: Symphonie Nr. 41 C-Dur „Jupiter" von W. A. Mozart

Blockweises Lesen

Diese Methode bietet sich in der Militär-Symphonie von Haydn an (Beispiel 3). In den T. 260-264 sind die Stimmen weitgehend parallel geführt, so dass man sie gut im Ganzen überblicken kann. In den Streichern haben wir einen homophonen Satz (d.h. alle Stimmen spielen den gleichen Rhythmus), der in den unteren Stimmen aus Tonwiederholungen besteht, während die erste Violine etwas bewegter ist. Gleichzeitig erklingen in den Bläserstimmen Liegetöne (d.h. lang ausgehaltene Töne), die als harmonischer Füllstoff dienen. Sie können bei Bedarf auch im Block gelesen werden.
Oft bestehen solche blockhaften Gebilde auch aus unisono-Figuren (= alle Stimmen spielen dasselbe), wie z.B. am Beginn der Jupiter-Symphonie von Mozart (Beispiel 4). Hier kann man sich beim Lesen zunächst nur auf den Streicherblock beschränken, der in den T. 3-4 alleine die Melodie weiterführt und bereits alle wichtigen Informationen enthält.

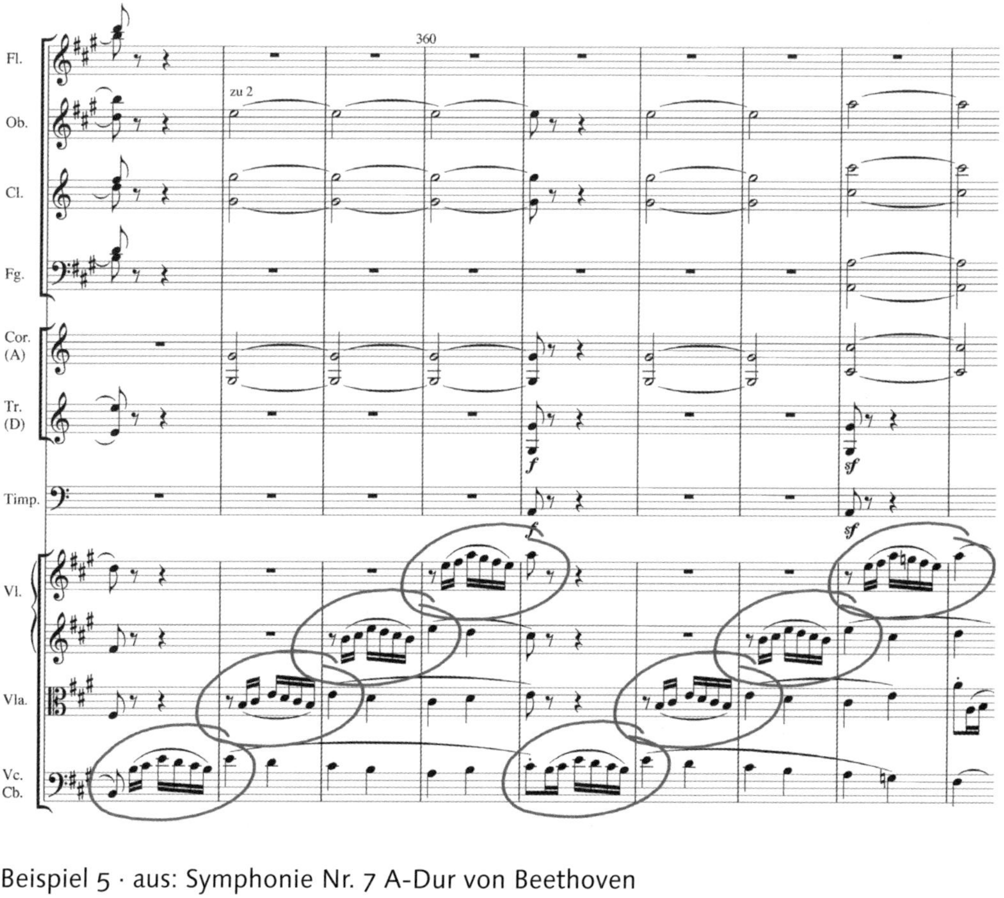

Beispiel 5 · aus: Symphonie Nr. 7 A-Dur von Beethoven

Selektives Lesen

Bei dieser Methode orientiert man sich anhand ausgewählter Stimmen (führende Stimmen, auffällige Stellen) in der Partitur. Im Ausschnitt aus Beethovens 7. Symphonie (Beispiel 5) ist hierzu das Sechzehntelmotiv geeignet, das zweimal von den Celli und Bässen ausgehend durch die Streicherstimmen wandert. Die Liegetöne der Bläser, die in den T. 358-363 sogar nur aus dem Ton e in unterschiedlichen Oktavlagen bestehen, bilden die harmonische Grundierung und spielen beim Lesen der Partitur eine untergeordnete Rolle. Man nimmt sie kurz wahr, verfolgt jedoch die Streicher und dort insbesondere das auffällige Sechzehntelmotiv in seiner Wanderung durch die einzelnen Stimmen.

Bei beiden Leseformen, zwischen denen man übrigens je nach Beschaffenheit der Stelle wechseln sollte, kommt es am Anfang nicht darauf an, sofort alle Töne und Harmonien verfolgen zu können. Viel wichtiger ist es, Bewegungsabläufe zu erkennen und nachzuvollziehen. Alles Weitere kommt mit der Erfahrung.

Verfolgen von kontrapunktischen Stimmen

Der vorliegende Ausschnitt aus Brahms' Requiem (Beispiel 6) ist polyphon komponiert, d.h. man muss mehrere gleichwertige Stimmen entweder im Wechsel (ohne den Anschluss zu verlieren) oder gleichzeitig verfolgen können.

Doch das auf den ersten Blick so übervolle Notenbild lichtet sich bald, wenn man sich die Partitur näher auf parallele Stimmen ansieht. Brahms ordnet z.B. jeder Chorstimme Orchesterstimmen zu. Das hat zur Folge, dass hier zwar viele Stimmen notiert sind, aber wesentlich weniger eigenständige Stimmen tatsächlich erklingen. Die vielen geschriebenen Noten lassen sich also auf ein überschaubares Maß reduzieren.

So werden Flöte, Klarinette, erste Violinen und Sopran parallel geführt. Des Weiteren wird der Tenor von Oboe und Bratsche mit einer stark erweiterten, aber dennoch parallel verlaufenden Stimme unterstützt. Ebenfalls fast ganz parallel verlaufen Violoncelli und Fagotte.

Zu den polyphon gefügten Stimmen erklingen die tiefen Bläser und Streicher sowie die Pauke mit Füllstimmen, welche lediglich aus Liegetönen (ausgehaltene Töne) bestehen. Sie braucht man beim ersten Lesen nicht weiter zu verfolgen.

Im Ganzen gesehen bietet sich in diesem Ausschnitt an, schwerpunktmäßig die Sopranstimme zu verfolgen, da sie mit zwei Instrumenten gekoppelt ist und als höchste Stimme gut herauszuhören ist. Zudem bietet der Text eine Orientierungshilfe, so dass der Wiedereinstieg von vorübergehenden Ausflügen in andere Stimmen erleichtert wird.

Bei fugierten Abschnitten kann man sich das Mitlesen auch erleichtern, indem man zunächst alle Einsätze des Themas in der Partitur sucht und sich markiert.

Beispiel 6 · aus: Ein deutsches Requiem von Brahms

Die Partitur im Überblick

A **Taktstriche** sind innerhalb der Instrumentengruppen durchgezogen.

B Die **Taktzahlen** erleichtern die Orientierung in der Partitur. Manchmal dienen hierzu auch Großbuchstaben, sog. Studierbuchstaben.

C Eine einzelne Zeile der Partitur nennt man **Notensystem**. Für welche(s) Instrument(e) sie steht, zeigt der **Instrumentenvorsatz** an (hier Fl. für Flöte).

D Der **Kopfstrich** verbindet alle Notensysteme miteinander zu einer **Akkolade**.

E Zusätzlich zum Kopfstrich fassen **gerade Klammern** die einzelnen Instrumentengruppen (Holz-, Blech- und Streichinstrumente) zusammen. Innerhalb dieser Gruppen sind die Instrumente nach Tonlage geordnet, wobei das höchste an oberster Stelle steht.
Die heute übliche Partituranordnung lautet von oben nach unten:
· Holzblasinstrumente
· Blechblasinstrumente
· Schlaginstrumente
· Harfe, Klavier, Celesta
· Soloinstrument(e)
· Solostimmen
· Chor
· Streichinstrumente

F Stehen zwei Akkoladen auf einer Seite, werden sie durch zwei **Schrägstriche** voneinander abgetrennt.

G Steht hinter dem Instrumentennamen z.B. „in B" oder (B), handelt es sich um ein **transponierendes Instrument**. In diesem Fall deutet das (B) an, dass das notierte C als B erklingt, also alle Noten einen Ton tiefer erklingen als sie notiert sind. Die meisten transponierenden Instrumente sind in der Partitur durch diese Zusätze leicht zu erkennen. Es gibt aber auch transponierende Instrumente ohne eine entsprechende Angabe in der Partitur, wie z.B.:
Piccoloflöte (in c/eine Oktave höher)
Englischhorn (in f/eine Quinte tiefer)
Kontrafagott (in c/eine Oktave tiefer)
Kontrabass (in c/eine Oktave tiefer)

H Die transponierenden Blechblasinstrumente haben keine Generalvorzeichen, sondern bei Bedarf Versetzungszeichen, die direkt vor der jeweiligen Note stehen.

I Die Viola oder Bratsche wird im **Alt- bzw. Bratschenschlüssel** notiert, die Stimmen des Violoncellos und Fagotts manchmal im **Tenorschlüssel**. Beide Schlüssel sind leicht zu lesen, wenn man sich klarmacht, dass der Schlüssel den Ton c1 umrahmt, also:

Alt- Tenor- Violinschlüssel

J Vor einem Wechsel der Ton- oder Taktart steht immer ein **Doppelstrich**. Das hier folgende Alla-Breve-Zeichen (¢) ist ebenso wie das Zeichen für den 4/4-Takt (c) ein Relikt aus einer älteren Notationspraxis und steht für den 2/2-Takt.

B
A
C
4
29
Fl.
Ob. 1 2
Cl. (B♭) 1 2
Fag. 1 2
Cor. (B♭) 1 2
Vl. I II
Vla.
Vc.
Cb.
D
E
sfp
dim.
pp
1.
arco
F
34
G
H
Tr. (B♭) 1 2
Timp.
ff
tr
cresc.
5
I
Vc. Cb.
J

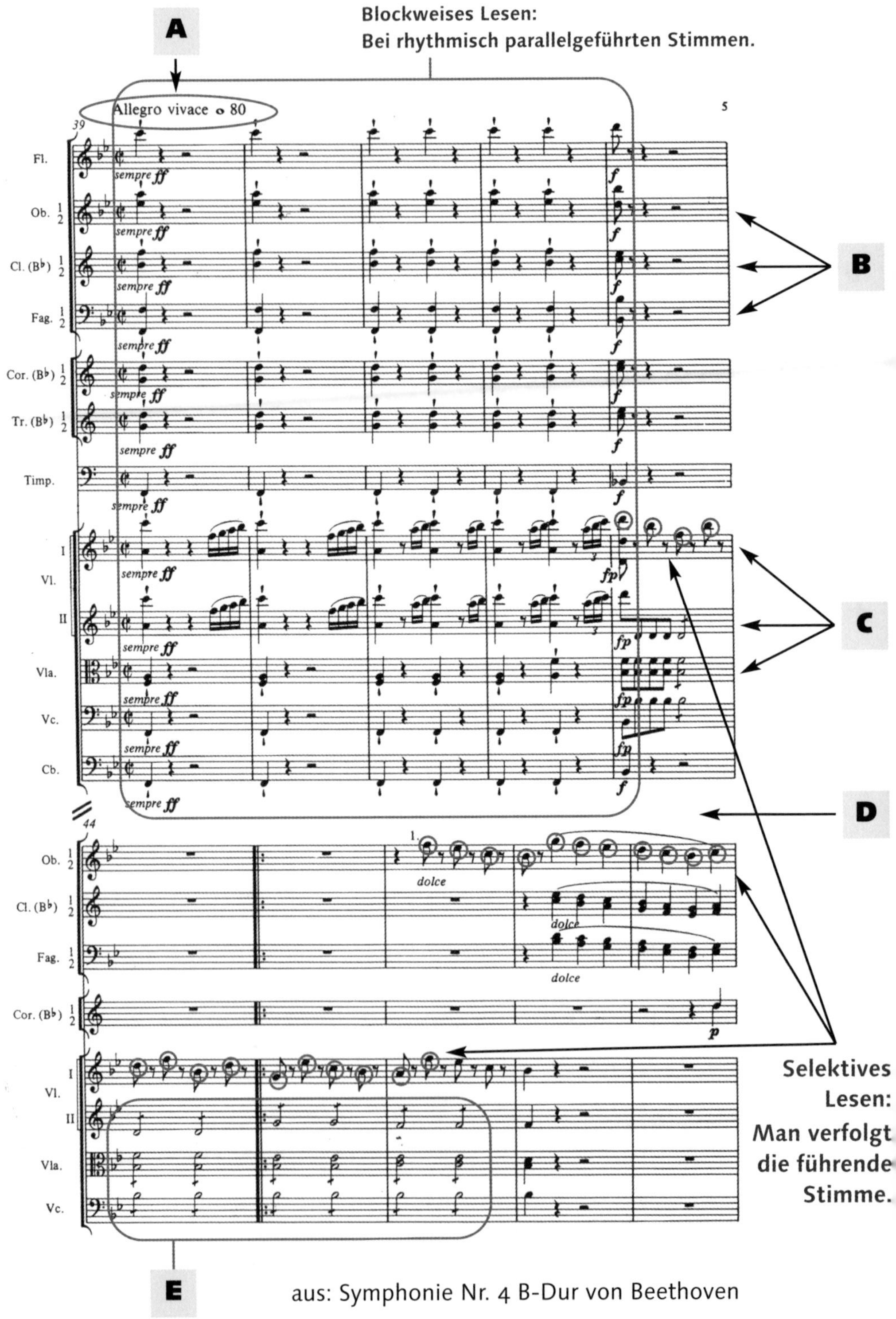

aus: Symphonie Nr. 4 B-Dur von Beethoven

A Durch die **Tempoangabe** (manchmal mit einer Metronomzahl verbunden) gibt der Komponist an, wie schnell ein Stück gespielt werden soll.

B Bei den Bläsern werden in der Regel zwei Stimmen in einer Notenzeile zusammengefasst. Spielen sie den gleichen Ton, erhält der Notenkopf zwei Hälse oder es steht a2 darüber.

C Zweistimmige Akkorde in den Notensystemen der Streicher werden von einem Spieler gespielt. Will man die Stimmen aufteilen, schreibt man **divisi** (geteilt). Dann spielt an jedem Pult ein Spieler die oberen und ein Spieler die unteren Noten.

D Hat eine Stimme, wie hier die Flöte, längere Zeit Pause, wird ihr Notensystem oft bis zum erneuten Einsatz der Stimme weggelassen. So wird Platz gespart, man muß weniger blättern und die erklingenden Stimmen sind übersichtlicher angeordnet.

E Um Platz zu sparen und Tonfolgen übersichtlicher zu gestalten, verwendet man gelegentlich sogenannte **Abbreviaturen (Faulenzer)**. Das hier verwendete Zeichen 𝅗𝅥 steht für ♩♩♩♩, wobei die Halbe Note die Dauer der Wiederholungen anzeigt und der Strich durch den Notenhals den Wert der zu wiederholenden Noten (1 Strich = Achtel, 2 = Sechzehntel usw.). Vgl. auch die Viola in T. 43, in der zunächst die Repetitionen ausgeschrieben und dann abgekürzt sind.

Partiturlesen im Klassensatz

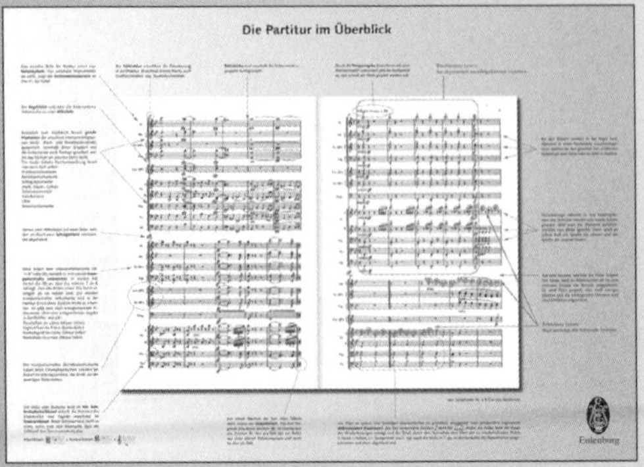

Diese kurze Einführung können Sie als kostenloses Faltblatt bestellen – gern auch im Klassensatz!

Faltblatt "Die Kunst des Partiturlesens"

Bestellnummer: ETP 9999-99 (kostenlos)

Die passende Ergänzung für Klassen- und Unterrichtsräume:

Plakat A2 "Die Partitur im Überblick"

Bestellnummer ETP 9950-99 (kostenlos)

Mozart im Klassensatz

Ein Lebens- und Reisebild

Mozart war nicht nur einer der größten Komponisten, sondern auch einer der besten Pianisten des 18. Jahrhunderts. Wie heutige Virtousen verbrachte er große Teile seines Lebens auf Konzertreisen zwischen den führenden Höfen und großen Städten seiner Zeit. Diese kleine Broschüre entfaltet ein Panorama des europäischen Musiklebens, das den Hintergrund für Mozarts Schaffen bildete. Eine Kurzbiographie und ein kleiner Einblick in seine Schreibweise runden das Bild ab.

Faltblatt "Mozart. Ein Lebens- und Reisebild"

Bestellnummer ETP 9990-99 (kostenlos)

Weitere Informationen unter www.eulenburg.de

Eulenburg